Cornish Fairies

Robert Hunt

Tor Mark • Redruth

For further information of all the titles in this series please visit:-
www.tormark.co.uk

Published by Tor Mark, United Downs Ind Est, Redruth, Cornwall TR16 5HY
First published 1995; this reprint 2009
© 1995 Tor Mark
ISBN 978 085025 351 1
The cover illustration is by Linda Garland
Printed by R Booth Ltd, The Praze, Penryn, Cornwall TR10 8AA

These stories are taken from Robert Hunt's *Popular Romances of the West Country* published in 1865. They had been collected some thirty years earlier. He had been determined that these 'drolls and romances', as he called them, should not be lost. For ten months he travelled throughout Cornwall 'listening at the hearths of country folk'.

These were the stories that had been handed down from generation to generation by word of mouth. In most instances this was the first time the tales had been recorded. Of course our forebears had no problem in believing in fairies or the 'little people'.

Other collections of Robert Hunt's stories are published in *Cornish Legends* and *Cornish Folklore* in this series.

The Elfin Creed

It should be understood that there are in Cornwall five varieties of the fairy family, clearly distinguishable:

1. The Small People;
2. The Spriggans;
3. Piskies, or Pigseys;
4. The Buccas, Bockles, or Knockers;
5. The Browneys.

Of the *Small People* I have heard two accounts. Indeed it is by no means clear that the tradition of their origin does not apply to the whole of the five branches of this ancient family. The Small People are believed by some to be the spirits of the people who inhabited Cornwall many thousands of years ago, long, long before the birth of Christ. That they were not good enough to inherit the joys of heaven, but that they were too good to be condemned to eternal fires. They were said to be 'poor innocents' (this phrase is now applied to silly children). When they first came into this land, they were much larger than they are now, but ever since the birth of Christ they have been getting smaller and smaller. Eventually they will turn into muryans (ants) and at last be lost from the face of the earth. These Small People are exceedingly playful amongst themselves, but they are usually demure when they know that any human eye sees them. They commonly aid those people to whom they take a fancy and, frequently, they have been known to perform the most friendly acts towards men and women. The above notion corresponds with the popular belief in Ireland, which is 'that the fairies are a portion of the fallen angels, who, being less guilty than the rest, were not driven to hell but were suffered to dwell on earth'. In Cornwall, as in Wales, another popular creed is that the fairies are Druids becoming – because they will not give up their idolatries – smaller and smaller. These Small People in many things closely resemble the Elves of Scandinavia.

The *Spriggans* are quite a different class of beings. In some respects they appear to be offshoots from the family of the Trolls of Sweden and Denmark. The Spriggans are found only about the cairns, quoits or cromlechs, burrows or detached stones, with which it is unlucky for humans to meddle. They are a remarkably mischievous and thievish tribe. If ever a house was robbed, a child stolen or cattle carried away, or a building demolished, it was the work of the Spriggans. Whatever commotion took place in earth, air or water, it was all put down as the work of these spirits. Wherever the giants have been, there the Spriggans have been also. It is usually considered that they are the ghosts of the giants; certainly, from many of their feats, we must suppose them to possess a giant's strength. The Spriggans have the charge of buried treasure.

The *Piskie*. This fairy is a most mischievous and very unsociable sprite. His favourite fun is to entice people into the bogs by appearing like the light from a cottage window, or as a man carrying a lantern. The piskie partakes, in many respects, of the character of the Spriggan. So wide-spread were their depredations, and so annoying their tricks, that it at one time was necessary to select persons whose acuteness and ready tact were a match for these quick-witted wanderers, and many a clever man has become famous for his power to give charms against Pigseys. It does not appear, however, that anything remarkable was required of the clever man. No Pigsey could harm a man if his coat were inside out, and it became a very common practice for persons who had to go from village to village by night to wear their jacket or cloak so turned, ostensibly to prevent the dew from taking the shine off the cloth, but in reality to render them safe from the Pigseys. They must have been a merry lot, for 'to laugh like a Piskie' is a popular saying. These little fellows were great plagues to the farmers, riding their colts, and chasing their cows.

The *Buccas* or *Knockers*. These are the sprites of the mines, and correspond to the Kobals of the German mines, the Duergars and the Trolls. They were said to be the souls of the Jews who formerly worked the tin-mines of Cornwall. They were not allowed to rest because of their wicked practices as tinners, and they shared in the general curse which ignorant people believe still hangs on this race.

The *Browney*. This spirit was purely of the household. Kindly and good, he devoted his every care to benefit the family with whom he had taken up his abode. The Browney has fled, owing to his having been brought into very close contact with the schoolmaster, and he is only summoned now upon the occasion of the swarming of the bees. When this occurs, mistress or maid seizes a bell-metal or a tin pan, and, beating it, she calls 'Browney,

Browney' as loud as she can until the good Browney compels the bees to settle.

Some writers have supposed that at the time of the Reformation the fairies departed from the land. This hypothesis is not warranted by the evidence. It is possible that they may have taken possession of some of the inferior creatures, but they are still to be found in those regions which lie beyond the railway-giant with his fiery mouth, or that electric spirit who, travelling on the mysterious wires, can beat the wildest elf that ever mounted 'night-steeds'.

The night riders

I was on a visit when a boy at a farmhouse situated near Fowey river. Well do I remember the farmer with much sorrow telling us one morning at breakfast, that 'the piskie people had been riding Tom again'. And this he regarded as certainly leading to the destruction of a fine young horse. There could be no doubt that the animal was much distressed, and refused to eat his food. The mane was said to be knotted into fairy stirrups; and Mr – told me he had no doubt at least twenty small people had sat upon the animal's neck. He even assured me that one of his men had seen them urging the horse to his utmost speed round and round one of his fields.

The piskies in the cellar

On the Thursday immediately preceding Christmas-tide (year not recorded) were assembled at 'The Rising Sun' the captain and men of a streamwork in the Couse below. This Couse was a flat alluvial moor, broken by gigantic mole-hills, the work of many a generation of tinners. One was half inclined, on looking at the turmoiled ground, to believe with them that the tin grew in successive crops, for, after years of turning and searching, there was still enough to give the landlord his dole and to furnish wages to some dozen streamers. The night was a festival in honour of one Picrous, and intended to celebrate the discovery of tin on this day by a man of that name. The feast is still kept, though it has dwindled to a supper and its attendant merry-making.

Our story has especially to do with the adventures of one of the party, John Sturtridge, who, well-primed with ale, started on his homeward way for Luxulyan Church-town. John had got as far as Tregarden Down without any mishap worth recording when, alas! he happed upon a party of the little people who were at their sports in the shelter of a huge granite boulder. Assailed by shouts of derisive laughter, he hastened on frightened and bewildered, but the Down, well known from earlier experience, became like ground untrodden, and after long trial no gate or stile was to be found. He was getting vexed as well as puzzled when a chorus of tiny voices shouted 'Ho! and away for Par Beach!' John repeated the shout and was in an instant caught up and in a twinkling found himself on the sands at Par. A brief dance, and the cry was given 'Ho! and away for Squire Tremain's cellar!' A repetition of the piskie cry found John with his elfish companions in the cellars at Heligan, where was beer and wine galore. It need not be said that he availed himself of his opportunities. The mixture of all the good liquors so affected him that, alas! he forgot in time to catch up the next cry of 'Ho! and away for Par Beach!'

In the morning John was found by the butler, groping and tumbling among butts and barrels, very much muddled with the squire's good drink. His strange story, very incoherently told, was not credited by the squire, who committed him to jail for the burglary, and in due time he was convicted and sentenced to death.

The morning of his execution arrived; a large crowd had assembled and John was standing under the gallows-tree when a commotion was observed in the crowd, and a little lady of commanding mien made her way through the opening throng to the scaffold. In a shrill sweet voice, which John recognised, she cried 'Ho! and away to France!' Which being replied to, he was rapt from the officers of justice, leaving them and the multitude mute with wonder and disappointment.

Changelings

A correspondent, to whom I am much indebted for many curious examples of the folk-lore of the people in the remote districts to the west of Penzance, says 'I never knew but one child that had been kept by the Spriggans for more than three days. It was always complaining, sickly and weakly, and had the very face of a changeling.'

It has been my own good fortune, some thirty or forty years since, to have seen several children of whom it has been whispered amongst the peasantry that they were changelings. In every case they have been sad examples of the influence of mesenteric [intestinal] disease – the countenance much altered – their eyes glassy and sunk in their sockets – the nose sharpened – the cheeks of a marble whiteness, unless when they were flushed with hectic fever – the lips sometimes swollen and of a deep red colour, and small ulcers not infrequently at the angles of the mouth. The wasted frame, with sometimes strumous swellings, and the unnatural abdominal enlargement which accompanies disease of mesenteric glands, gives a very sad, and often most unnatural appearance to the sufferer. The intense ignorance which existed in many parts of the district visited by me, at the period named [c 1825], has been almost dispelled by the civilising influences of Wesleyanism. Consequently when a scrofulous child is found in a family, we no longer hear of its being a changeling; but within a very recent period I have heard it said that such afflicted children had been 'ill-wished'.

The piskies' changeling

There is a farmhouse of some antiquity with which my family have a close connection; and it is this circumstance more than any other that has rendered this tradition concerning it more interesting to us, and better remembered, than many others equally romantic and authentic.

Close to this house, one day, a miserable looking bantling was discovered alone, unknown, and incapable of making its wants understood. It was instantly remembered by the finder that this was the way the piskies were accustomed to deal with those infants of their race for whom they sought human protection; and it would have been an awful circumstance if such a one were not received by the individual so visited. The anger of the piskies would be certain, and some direful calamity must be the result; whereas a kind welcome would probably be attended with great good fortune. The miserable plight of this stranger, therefore, attracted attention and sympathy. The little unconscious one was admitted as one of the family. Its health was speedily restored, and its renewed strength, activity, intelligence and good humour caused it to become a general favourite. It is true the stranger was often found to indulge in odd freaks; but this was accounted for by a recollection of its pedigree, which was not doubted to be of the piskie order. So the family prospered, and had banished the thought that the foundling would ever leave them. There was to the front door of this house, a hatch, which is a half-door that is kept closed when the whole door behind it is open, and it then serves as a guard against the intrusion of dogs, hogs and ducks while air and light are freely admitted. This little being was one day leaning over the top of this hatch, and looking wistfully outward, when a clear voice was heard to proceed from a neighbouring part of the townplace, calling 'Coleman Gray, Coleman Gray!' The piskie immediately started up and, with a sudden laugh, clapped its hands, exclaiming, 'Aha! my daddy is come!' It was gone in a moment, never to be seen again.

The pixies of Dartmoor

There is a celebrated piskie haunt at Costellas in Cornwall (says Mrs Bray) where they have been seen sitting in a ring – the men smoking after the most approved fashion of the Dutch burgomaster, and the women spinning, perhaps in emulation of the frugal vow.

I never heard of this place. Like the rest of the 'good people', piskies are fond of music, and the sound of their 'harp and pipe and symphony' is occasionally heard at nightfall. It is said that a man once passing one of the piskie rings, and hearing them dancing and singing within it, threw a large stone into the midst of the circle, when the music at once ceased and a dreadful shriek arose.

The appearance of the pixies (for so they are called in Devon) of Dartmoor is said to resemble that of a bale or bundle of rags. In this shape they decoy children to their unreal pleasure. A woman on the northern borders of the moor was returning home late on a dark evening, accompanied by two children and carrying a third in her arms, when on arriving at her own door she found one missing. Her neighbours, with lanthorns, immediately set out in quest of the lost child whom they found sitting under a large oak-tree, well known to be a favourite haunt of the pixies. He declared that he had been led away by two large bundles of rags which had remained with him until the lights appeared, when they had immediately vanished.

The pixies of Dartmoor, notwithstanding their darker character, aided occasionally in household work. A washerwoman was one morning greatly surprised, on coming downstairs, to find all her clothes neatly washed and folded. She watched the next evening, and observed a pixie in the act of performing this kind office for her; but she was ragged and mean in appearance, and Betty's gratitude was sufficiently great to induce her to prepare a yellow petticoat and a red cap for the obliging pixie.

The fairy revels on the 'Gump', St Just

Long has the Gump been the reputed playground of the Small People. Many of the good old people were permitted to witness their revels, and for years they have delighted their grand-children with tales of the songs they have heard, and of the sights they have seen. To many of their friends those fairies have given small but valuable presents; but woe to the man or woman who would dare to intrude upon the ground occupied by them at the time of their high festivals. There was a covetous old hunks in St Just – never mind his name, he was severely punished, let that suffice – well, this old fellow had heard so much of the riches displayed by the little people, when holding holiday on the Gump, that he determined to get some of the treasures.

He learned all he could from his neighbours, but kept his intention to himself. It was during the harvest moon – the night was a softened day – and everything abroad on such a night should have been in harmony with its quiet brilliancy. But here was a dark soul passing along, making a small eclipse with his black shadow. The old man stole towards the rendezvous of the 'good people', as some were fond of calling them, anxiously looking out for the treasures which he coveted. At length, when he had not advanced far on the Gump, he heard music of a most ravishing kind. Its influence was of a singularly mysterious character. As the notes were solemn and slow, or quick and gay, the old man was moved from tears to laughter; and on more than one occasion he was compelled to dance in obedience to the time. Notwithstanding that he was almost bewildered by the whirling motion to which he was compelled, the old man 'kept his wits awake' and waited his opportunity to seize some fairy treasure; but as yet nothing remarkable had presented itself. The music appeared to surround him and, as he thought, to come closer to him than it was at first; and although its sound led him to believe that the musicians were on the surface, he was impressed with an idea that they were really beneath the earth. Eventually there was a crash of sound, startling beyond description, and the hill before him opened. All was now ablaze with variously coloured lights. Every blade of grass was hung with lamps, and every furze bush was illuminated with stars. Out from the opening in the hill marched a host of spriggans, as if to clear the road. Then came an immense number of musicians playing on every kind of instrument. These were followed by troop after troop of soldiers, each troop bearing aloft their banner, which appeared to spread itself, to display its blazonry, without the assistance of any breeze. All these arranged themselves in order over the ground, some here and some there. One thing was not at all to our friend's liking: several hundreds of the most grotesque of the spriggans placed themselves so as to enclose the spot on which he was standing. Yet, as they were none of them higher than his shoe-tie, he thought he could squash them easily enough with his foot if they were up to any mischief, and so he consoled himself. This vast array having disposed of themselves, first came a crowd of servants bearing vessels of silver and vessels of gold, goblets cut out of diamonds, rubies, and other precious stones. There were others laden, almost to overflowing, with the richest meats, pastry, preserves and fruits. Presently the ground was covered with tables and everything was arranged with the most systematic order – each party falling back as they disposed of their burdens.

The brilliancy of the scene nearly overpowered the old man; but, when he was least prepared for it, the illumination became a thousand times more intense. Out of the hill were crowding thousands upon thousands of lovely ladies and gentlemen, arrayed in the most costly attire. He thought there would be no end to the coming crowd. By and by, however, the music suddenly changed, and the harmonious sounds which fell upon his ears appeared to give new life to every sense. His eyes were clearer, his ears quicker, and his sense of smell more exquisite. The odours of flowers, more delicious than any he had ever smelt, filled the air. He saw, without any disturbing medium, the brilliant beauty of the thousands of ladies who were now upon the Gump; and their voices were united in one gush of song, which was as clear as silver bells – a hymeneal symphony of the utmost delicacy. The words were in a language unknown to him, but he saw they were directed towards a new group now emerging from the hill.

First came a great number of female children, clothed in whitest gauze, strewing flowers on the Gump. These were not dead or cut flowers, for the moment they touched the ground they took root and grew. These were followed by an equally large number of boys, holding in their hands shells which seemed to be strung like harps, and from which they brought forth murmurs of melody such as angels only could hope to hear and live. Then came – and there was no end to their coming – line upon line of little men clothed in green and gold, and, by and by, a forest of banners, which at a signal were all furled. Then, seated upon thrones, carried on a platform above the heads of the men, came a young prince and princess who blazed with beauty and jewels as if they were suns amidst a skyey host of stars. There was much ceremonial marching to and fro, but eventually the platform was placed on amound on the Gump, which was now transformed into a hillock of roses and lilies; and around this all the ladies and gentlemen walked, bowing, and each one saying something to the princess and prince – passing onward and taking their seats at the tables.

Although no man could count the number of this fairy host, there was no confusion; all the ladies and gentlemen found, as if by instinct, their places. When all were seated, a signal was given by the prince; servants in splendid liveries placed tables crowded with gold-plate and good things on the platform, and everyone, prince and princess included, began to feast with a will.

Well, thought the old man, now is my time; if I could only crawl up to the prince's table, I should have a catch sure enough, and become a rich man for life. With his greedy mind fixed on this one object, and unobservant of everything else, he crouched down as though by so doing he could escape observation, and very slowly and stealthily advanced amongst the revellers. He never saw that thousands of spriggans had thrown little strings about him, and that they still held the ends of the threads. The presence of this selfish old mortal did not in any way discompose the assembly; they ate and drank and were as merry as though no human eye was looking on them. The old man was wondrous cautious lest he should disturb the feasters, consequently a long time was spent in getting, as he desired, to the back of the mound. At length he reached the desired spot and, to his surprise, everything was dark and gloomy behind him, but in front of the mound, all was a blaze of light. Crawling like a serpent on his belly, trembling with anxiety, the old man advanced close to the prince and princess. He was somewhat startled to find, as he looked out over the mound, that every one of the thousands of eyes in that multitude was fixed on his. He gazed a while, all the time screwing his courage up; then, as a boy who would catch a butterfly, he took off his hat and carefully raised it, so as to cover the prince, the princess, and their costly table, and, when about to close it upon them, a shrill whistle was heard, the old man's hand was fixed powerless in the air, and everything became dark around him.

Whir! whir! whir! as if a flight of bees were passing him buzzed in his ears. Every limb, from head to foot, was as if stuck full of pins and pinched with tweezers. He could not move, he was chained to the ground. By some means he had rolled down the mound, and lay on his back with his arms outstretched, arms and legs being secured by magic chains to the earth; therefore, he suffered great agony, he could not stir, and strange enough, his tongue appeared to be tied by cords so that he could not call. He had lain, no one can tell how long, in this sad plight, when he felt as if a number of insects were running over him, and by the light of the moon he saw standing on his nose one of the spriggans, who looked exceedingly like a small dragonfly. This little monster stamped and jumped with great delight; and having had his own fun upon the elevated piece of humanity, he laughed most outrageously, and shouted, 'Away, away, I smell the day!' Upon this the army of small people who had taken possession of the old man's body moved quickly away, and left our discomfited hero alone on the Gump. Bewildered, or, as he said, bedevilled, he lay still to gather up his thoughts. At length the sun arose, and then he found that he had been tied to the ground by myriads of gossamer webs, which were now covered with dew, and glistened like diamonds in the sunshine.

He shook himself and was free. He rose, wet, cold and ashamed. Sulkily he made his way to his home. It was a long time before his friends could learn from the old man where he had passed the night, but by slow degrees they gathered the story as I have told it to you.

Betty Stogs and Jan the Mounster

In the 'high countries', as the parishes of Morva, Zennor and Towednack are called, there has long existed a tradition that the children of dirty, lazy, 'courseying' women are often taken away by the Small People, carefully cleansed and then returned – of course all the more beautiful for being washed by the fairies in morning dew. This notion has evidently prevailed for many ages, and, like many an old tradition, it has been remodelled in each generation to adapt it to the conditions of the time. The following is but slightly modified in its characteristics from a story, somewhat coarsely told and greatly extended, by an old woman in Morva.

A woman, up the higher side, called Betty Stogs, very nearly lost her baby a few months ago. Stogs was only a nickname, but everyone knew her by that and no other. It was given to her because she was so untidy about the feet and legs. She could not darn a hole in her stocking – the lazy slut could never knit one.

Betty was always pulling the legs of her stockings down under her feet, that the holes in her heels might not be seen – as long as the tops would come under the garter – and she often gartered halfway down the leg to meet the necessities of the case. Betty was reared up in Towednack, at no great distance from Wheal Reeth, at which bal the old man her father worked. He also farmed a few acres of land, and, 'out of care', he and his daughter worked on it. The old people used to say they wouldn't put the poor innocent chield to work to bal, for fear the great rough heathens from Lelant might overcome her; so they kept her at home, and the old man would brag about how his Betty could cut furze and turf. Instead of staying at home in the evenings, Betty was always racing round the lanes to class meetings; for she had been 'a professor [committed Methodist] ever since she was a chield'. Betty was an only child, and the old people had saved a little money, and they hoped that some one 'above the common' would marry her. In Higher Side there lived a man called Jan the Mounster and, tempted by the bit of money, he resolved to lay himself out to catch Betty. Jan became a converted character – he met in the same class with Betty and expressed himself as being 'so fond of the means of grace'.

Things went on in this way for some time, and it was found that Betty had 'met with a misfortune'. The old people were now in a great hurry to marry their daughter, and promised Jan money enough to buy a set of china and lots of beautiful clome [earthenware], but Mounster required more than this and fought off. He left the 'people' so that he might not be read out [publicly denounced and expelled from the Church]. He said he was heartily sick of the lot, told strange stories about their doings, and became as bad a character as ever.

Time advanced, and Betty's mother – who was herself a wretchedly dirty woman and, as people said, too fond of the drop of drink – saw that she must lose no chance of making her daughter an honest woman. So she went to Penzance and bought a new bed – a real four-poster – and new dresser, painted bright lead and liver colour – an eight-day clock in a painted mahogany case – a mass of beautiful clome – and a glass milk cup. When all these things were ranged in a cottage, Jan was well enough pleased with them, and hung his 'great turnip of a watch' up in the middle of the dresser, to see how it would look. When he had satisfied himself, he told the old woman that he would marry Betty out of hand if she would give them her great, pretty, bright warming pan to hang opposite the door. This was soon settled and the Mounster and Betty Stogs were married.

In a little time the voice of a baby was heard in Jan's cottage, but the poor child had no cradle, only a 'costan' [a straw and bramble basket]; and in addition to the ordinary causes of neglect, another cause was introduced – Betty took to drink. A great, nasty suss of a woman – who went about pretending to sell crochet-work, but in reality to sell gin which she kept in a bottle under the dirty rags, which she called 'the most beautiful croshar work collars and cuffs that all the ladies in the towns and up the country wear on Sundays and high holidays' – formed a close acquaintance with Jan's wife. The result was, things went from bad to worse. Jan was discontented and went to bal and returned from bal always a sullen man. One day Betty had to bake some bread – she had never before done so, as her mother had always attended to that job. Jan had left his watch hanging to the dresser, that Betty might know the time. All went well to the middle of the day, and, just as the bread was ready to put down, in came the crochet woman.

First Betty had a noggin of gin – she then had her fortune told – and because she was promised no end of good luck and the handsomest children in the country, and Jan the best luck in tribute pitches, the kettle was boiled and some pork fried for the fortune-teller.

All this time the dough was forgotten, and it was getting sour and heavy. At last, when the woman went away, the lump of sour leven was put down to bake. The neglected child got troublesome, and as Jan would be home early to supper, Betty was in a great hurry to get things done. To quiet the child she gave it Jan's watch; and that it might be the better pleased, she opened it, 'that the dear chield might see the pretty little wheels spinning round'.

In a short time the watch was thrown down in the ashes, and it of course stopped. Betty at last wished to know the time; she then found the watch clogged full of dirt. To put the thing right she washed it out in the kettle of dish water, which had not been changed for two or three days and was thick with salt pilchard bones and pilchard skins. She did her best to clean the watch, for she was now terribly afraid of Jan, and she wiped all the little wheels, as far as she could reach, with the corner of the dish cloth, but the confounded thing would not go. She had to bake the bread by guess; and therefore when she took it up, it was black as soot and as hard as a stone.

Jan came home; and you may judge the temper he was in at finding things as they were, and his watch stopped. Betty swore to the deepest that she had never taken the thing into her hands. Next morning Jan got up early to go to bal; and taking the burnt loaf, he tried to cut it with his knife but it was in vain – as well try to cut a stone – next he tried the dag [axe] and Mounster said it strook fire, and the dag never made the least mark in the crust. The poor fellow had to go to his work without his breakfast, and to depend on the share of a comrade's fuggun for dinner.

Next day, Friday, was pay-day, and Jan having got his pay went to St Ives for bread, and took the precious watch with him to be set to rights. The watchmaker soon found out the complaint; here was a bit of fish bone, there a bit of potato paring; in one tooth a piece of worsted from a dish cloth, in another a particle of straw, and ashes everywhere.

The murder was out; and that night Jan, having first drunk to excess in St Ives, went home and nearly murdered his wife. From that time Jan was drunk every day, and Betty was, so often as she could get gin. The poor child was left half the day to suck his thumbs, and to tumble and toss on the filthy rags in the old costan, without anyone to look after it.

One day Betty was in a 'courseying' mood, and went from house to house, wherever she could find a woman idle enough to gossip with her. Betty stayed away till dark – it was Jan's last core by day – and the poor child was left all alone. When she came home she was surprised not to hear the child, but she thought it might have cried itself to sleep, and was not concerned. At last, having lit the candle, she looked in the costan, and there was no child to be seen. Betty searched about, in and out, every place she could think of; still there were no signs of the child; this pretty well sobered Betty, and she remembered that she had had to unlock the door to get into the cottage.

While yet full of fear and trembling to meet her husband, Jan came home from bal. He was, of course, told that his 'croom of a chield was lost'. He didn't believe a word of what Betty told him, but he went about and called up all the neighbours, who joined him in the search. They spent the night examining every spot around the house, and in the village – all in vain.

After daybreak they were all assembled in deep, and earnest consultation, when the cat came running into the house, with her tail on end and mewing anxiously. She ran forth and back round a brake of furze, constantly crying, as if she wished the people to follow her. After a long time, some one thought of going after the cat, and in the middle of the furze brake, on a beautiful green soft spot of mossy grass, was the baby sleeping, 'as sweet as a little nut', wrapped carefully up in some old dry gowns, and all its clothes neat and dry. When they unwrapped the child, they found he was covered all over with bright flowers, as we place them round a babe in the coffin. He had a bunch of violets in his dear little hands, and there were wallflowers and primroses, and balm and mint, spread over his body. The furze was high all around, so that no cold wind could reach the infant. Everyone declared that the child never looked so handsome before. It was plain enough, said the old women, that the Small People had taken the child and washed it from top to toe; that their task of cleansing the babe was a long one, and that the sun arose before they could finish it; that they had placed the child where it was found, intending to take it away the next night.

They were never known to come for the babe, but everyone said that this affair worked a great change in Betty Stogs and in Jan the Mounster. The cottage was kept tidy; the child clean; and its father and mother drank less and lived happier for ever afterwards.

The fairy ointment

Many years since, there lived as housekeeper with a celebrated squire, whose name is associated with the history of his native country, one Nancy Tregier. There were many peculiarities about Nancy; and she was, being a favourite with her master, allowed to do much as she pleased. She was in fact a petted, and consequently a spoiled, servant. Nancy left Pendeen one Saturday afternoon to walk to Penzance for the purpose of buying a pair of shoes. There was an old woman, Jenny Trayer, living in Pendeen Cove, who had the reputation of being a witch, or, as some people mildly put it, 'who had strange dealings'; and with her Nancy desired, for sundry reasons best known to herself, to keep on the closest of terms. So on this Saturday Nancy first called on the old woman to enquire whether she wished to have anything brought home from Penzance. Tom, the husband of Nancy's friend, did no work; but now and then he would go to sea for an hour or two and fish. It is true everybody gave Jenny just what she asked for her fish, out of pure fear. Sometimes they had a 'venture' with the smugglers, who in those days carried on a roaring trade in Pendeen Cove. The old Squire was a justice; but he winked very hard and didn't know anything about the smugglers. Indeed some ill-natured people − and there are always some such to be found in any nook or corner − said Nancy often took her master home a choice bottle of Cognac; even a case of 'Hollands' now and then; and, especially when there was to be a particularly great run, there were some beautiful silk handkerchiefs to be seen at the Squire's. But this is beyond our story. When Nancy went into Jenny's cottage, Tom was there, and right busy was she preparing some ointment and touching her husband's eyes with it; this Jenny tried to hide in the mouth of the oven by the side of the chimney. Tom got up and said he must be off, and left the two women together. After a few idle compliments, Jenny said that Nancy must have something to drink before she started for Penzance, and she went to the spence [pantry] for the bottle. Nancy, ever curious, seized the moment, dipped her finger in the pot of green ointment, and, thinking it was good for the eyes, she just touched her right eye with it before Jenny returned. They then took a horn or two together, and being thus spliced, Nancy started for Penzance.

Penzance market was in those days entirely in the street; even the old market house had not yet an existence. Nancy walked about doing a little business and a great deal of gossiping, when amongst the standings in Market Jew Street, whom should Nancy see but Tom Trayer, picking off the standings shoes, stockings, hanks of yarn and pewter spoons – indeed, some of all the sorts of things which were for sale. Nancy walked up to him, and, taking him by the arm, said 'Tom! ar'then't thee ashamed to be here carrying on such a game? However thee canst have the impudence I can't think, to be picking the things from the standings and putting them in thy pocket in broad daylight, and the people all around thee.' Tom looked very much surprised when Nancy spoke to him. At last he said, 'Is that you, Nancy? Which eye can you see me upon?' Nancy shut her left eye, this made no difference; she then shut her right eye and, greatly to her surprise, she saw all the people but she no longer saw Tom. She opened her right eye, and there was Tom as before. She winked, and winked, and was surprised you may be sure to find that she could not see Tom with both eyes. 'Now, Nancy,' said Tom, 'right or left?' 'Well', said Nancy, 'tis strange, but there is something wrong with my left eye.'

'Oh, then, you see me with the right, do you.'

Then Tom put his finger on her right eye, and from that moment she was blind on that side. On her way home, Nancy was always going off the road on her blind side, but the hedges kept her from wandering far away. On the downs near Pendeen there were no hedges, so Nancy wandered into a furze brake; night came on, she could not find her way out, and she was found in it the next morning fast asleep. The old Squire was out hunting in the early morning, according to his custom. In passing along the road leading to Carnyorth, he saw a woman's knitting work hanging on a bramble, and the yarn from the stocking leading away into the brake. He took the yarn in his hand, and followed it until he came to the old woman, asleep with the ball in her pocket. When the squire awakened her, Nancy told the story which I have told you. Her master, however, said he did not believe she had been in Penzance at all, but that she had stayed in the cove and got drunk; that when dark night came she had endeavoured to find her way home – had lost her road, fallen down and probed her eye out on a furze bush, and then gone off in drunken unconsciousness. Nancy told her master he was no better than an unbelieving heathen, and to the day of her death she protested that Tom Trayer put her eye out.

Jenny's ointment is said to have been made with a four-leafed clover, gathered at a certain time of the moon. This rendered Fairyland visible and made men invisible.

The fairy widower

Not many years since, a very pretty girl called Jenny Permuen lived in Towednack. She was of poor parents and lived in service. There was a good deal of romance, or what the old people called nonsense, in Jenny. She was always smartly dressed, and she would arrange wild flowers in her hair. As a consequence, Jenny attracted much of the attention of the young men, and again, as a consequence, a great deal of envy from the young women. Jenny was, no doubt, vain; and her vanity, which most vain persons will say is not unusual, was accompanied by a considerable amount of weakness on any point connected with her person. Jenny loved flattery, and being a poor, uneducated girl, she had not the genius necessary to disguise her frailty. When any man told her she was lovely, she quite admitted the truth of the assertion by her pleased looks. When any woman told her not to be such a fool as to believe such nonsense, her lips, and eyes too, seemed to say, you are only jealous of me, and if there was a pool of water near, nature's mirror was speedily consulted to prove to herself that she was really the best-looking girl in the parish.

Well, one day Jenny, who had been for some time out of a situation, was sent by her mother down to the lower parishes to look for a place. Jenny went on merrily enough until she came to the four cross roads on the Lady Downs, when she discovered that she knew not which road to take. She looked first one way and then another, and she felt fairly puzzled, so she sat down on a boulder of granite and began, in pure want of thought, to break off the beautiful fronds of ferns which grew abundantly around the spot she had chosen.

It is hard to say what her intentions were, whether to go on, to return, or to remain where she was, so utterly indifferent did Jenny appear. Some say she was entirely lost in wild dreams of self-gratification. However she had not long sat on this granite stone, when hearing a voice near her, she turned round, and saw a young man.

'Well, young woman,' says he, 'and what are you after?'

'I am after a place, sir,' says she.

'And what kind of place do you want, my pretty young woman?' says he, with the most winning smile in the world.

'I am not particular, sir,' says Jenny. 'I can make myself generally useful.'

'Indeed,' says the stranger; 'do you think you could look after a widower with one small boy?'

'I am very fond of children,' says Jenny.

'Well then,' says the widower, 'I wish to hire for a year and a day a young woman of your age, to take charge of my little boy.'

'And where do you live,' inquired Jenny.

'Not far from here,' said the man. 'Will you go with me and see?'

'An it please you to show me,' said Jenny.

'But first, Jenny Permuen –' Jenny stared when she found the stranger knew her name. He was evidently an entire stranger in the parish, and how could he have learnt her name, she thought. So she looked at him somewhat astonished. 'Oh! I see, you suppose I didn't know you; but do you think a young widower could pass through Towednack and not be struck with such a pretty girl? Beside,' he said, 'I watched you one day dressing your hair in one of my ponds, and stealing some of my sweet-scented violets to put in those lovely tresses. Now, Jenny Permuen, will you take the place?'

'For a year and a day?' asked Jenny.

'Yes, and if we are pleased with each other then, we can renew the engagement.'

'Wages,' said Jenny.

The widower rattled the gold in his breeches pocket.

'Wages! Well, whatever you like to ask,' said the man.

Jenny was charmed; all sorts of visions rose before her eyes, and without hesitation she said –

'Well, I'll take the place, sir; when must I come?'

'I require you now – my little boy is very unhappy, and I think you can make him happy again. You'll come at once?'

'But mother –'

'Never mind mother, I'll send word to her.'

'But my clothes –'

'The clothes you have will be all you require, and I'll put you in a much gayer livery soon.'

'Well then,' says Jenny, 'it's a bargain.'

'Not yet,' says the man, 'I have got a way of my own, and you must swear an oath.'

Jenny looked frightened.

'You need not be alarmed,' said the man very kindly; 'I only wish you to kiss that fern-leaf which you have in your hand, and say, "For a year and a day I promise to stay."'

'Is that all?' said Jenny; so she kissed the fern-leaf and said, 'For a year and a day I promise to stay.'

Without another word he walked forward on the road leading east-ward. Jenny followed him – she thought it strange that her new master never opened his lips to her all the way, and she grew very tired with walking. Still onward and onward he went, and Jenny was sadly weary and her feet dreadfully sore. At last poor Jenny began to cry. He heard her sob and looked round.

'Tired are you, poor girl? Sit down – sit down,' says the man; and he took her by the hand and led her to a mossy bank. His kindness completely overcame her, and she burst into a flood of tears. He allowed her to cry for a few minutes, then taking a bunch of leaves from the bottom of the bank, he said, 'Now I must dry your eyes, Jenny.'

He passed the bunch of leaves first over one and then over the other eye.

The tears were gone. Her weariness was departed. She felt herself moving, yet she did not know that she had moved from the bank. The ground appeared to open, and they were passing very rapidly under the earth. At last there was a pause.

'Here we are, Jenny,' said he, 'there is yet a tear of sorrow on your eyelids, and no human tears can enter our dwellings. Let me wipe them away.' Again Jenny's eyes were brushed with the small leaves as before, and lo! before her was such a country as she had never seen previously. Hill and valley were covered with flowers, strangely varied in colour but combining into a most harmonious whole; so that the region appeared sown with gems which glittered in the light of a summer sun, yet as mild as the moonlight. There were rivers clearer than any water she had ever seen on the granite hills, and waterfalls and fountains, while everywhere ladies and gentlemen dressed in green and gold were walking, or sporting, or reposing on banks of flowers, singing songs or telling stories. Oh! it was a beautiful world.

'Here we are at home,' said Jenny's master; and strangely enough he too was changed; he was the most beautiful little man she had ever seen, and he wore a green silken coat covered in ornaments of gold. 'Now,' said he again, 'I must introduce you to your little charge.' He led Jenny into a noble mansion in which all the furniture was of pearl and ivory, inlaid with gold and silver, and studded with emeralds. After passing through many rooms, they came at length to one which was hung all over with lace, as fine as the finest cobweb, most beautifully worked with flowers; and in the middle of this room was a little cot made out of some beautiful sea-shell, which reflected so many colours that Jenny could hardly bear to look at it. She was led to the side of this and she saw, as she said, 'one of God's sweetest angels sleeping there.' The little boy was so beautiful that she was ravished with delight.

'This is your charge,' said the father. 'I am the king in this land and I have my own reasons for wishing my boy to know something of human nature. Now you have nothing to do but wash and dress the boy when he wakes, to take him to walk in the garden, and to put him to bed when he is weary.'

Jenny entered on her duties and gave, and continued to give, satisfaction. She loved the darling little boy, and he appeared to love her, and the time passed away with astonishing rapidity.

Somehow or other she had never thought of her mother. She had never thought of her home at all. She was happy and in luxury, and never reckoned the passing of time.

Howsoever happiness may blind us to the fact, the hours and days move onward. The period for which Jenny had bound herself was gone, and one morning she awoke and all was changed. She was sleeping in her own bed in her mother's cottage. Everything was strange to her and she appeared strange to everybody. Numerous old gossips were called in to see Jenny, and to all Jenny told her strange tale alike. One day, old Mary Calineck of Zennor came, and she heard, as all the others had done, the story of the widower, and the baby, and the beautiful country. Some of the old crones who were there at the time, said the girl was 'gone clean daft'. Mary looked very wise.

'Crook your arm, Jenny,' said she. Jenny sat up in the bed and bent her arm, resting her hand on her hip. 'Now say, I hope my arm may never uncrook if I have told ye a word of a lie.'

'I hope my arm may never uncrook if I have told ye a word of a lie,' repeated Jenny.

'Uncrook your arm,' said Mary.

Jenny stretched out her arm.

'It is truth the girl is telling,' said Mary, and she has been carried by the small people to some of their countries under the hills.'

'Will the girl ever come right in her mind?' asked her mother.

'All in good time,' said Mary; 'and if she will but be honest, I have no doubt but her master will take care that she never wants.'

Howbeit, Jenny did not get on very well in the world. She married and was discontented and far from happy. Some said she always pined after the fairy widower. Others said they were sure she had misbehaved herself, or she would have brought back lots of gold. If Jenny had not dreamt all this, while she was sitting picking ferns on the granite boulder, she had certainly had a very strange adventure.

St Levan fairies

Years since – the time is passed now – the Green outside the gate at the end of Trezidder Lane was a favourite place with the Small Folks as a place to hold their fairs. One might often see the rings in the grass, which they made in dancing, when they footed it. Mr Trezillian was returning late one night from Penzance; when he came near the gate he saw a number of little creatures spinning round and round. The sight made him light-headed, but he could not resist the desire to be amongst them, so he got off his horse. In a moment they were all over him like a swarm of bees, and he felt as if they were sticking needles and pins into him. His horse ran off and he did not know what to do, till, by good luck, he thought of what he had often heard, so he turned his glove inside out, threw it amongst the Small Folk, and ere the glove reached the ground they were all gone. Mr Trezillian had now to find his horse, and the Small Folk, still determined to lead him a dance, bewildered him. He was piskie led, and he could not find out where he was until broad daylight. Then he saw he was not a hundred yards from the place he had left his horse. On looking round the spot where he had seen the Small Folk dancing, he found a pair of very small silver knee-buckles of most ancient shape, which, no doubt, some little gentleman must have lost when he was punishing the farmer. Those who knew the families will remember the little silver buckles, which were kept for some time at Trezidder and some time at Raftra.

Down in Penberth Cove lived an old woman who was a special favourite with these little people. She was a good old creature, and had been for many years bed-ridden. These small folk were her only company. Her relations dropped in once a day, rendered her the little aid she required, and left food by the bed-side. But day by day, and all the day long, the Small Folk vied with each other to amuse her. The men, she related, were for the most part dressed in green, with a red or a blue cap and a feather; 'They look for all the world like little sodgers.' As for the ladies – you should have heard the old woman tell of the gay ladies, with their feathers, hooped petticoats with furbelows, trains and fans, and what saucy little creatures they were with the men! No sooner was the old woman left alone than in they came and began their frolics, dancing over the rafters and key-beams, swinging by the cobwebs like rope dancers, catching the mice and riding them in and out through the holes in the thatch. When one party got tired another party came, and by daylight and even by moonlight, the old bed-ridden creature never wanted amusement.

The adventure of Cherry of Zennor

This may be regarded as another version of the story of the fairy widower, but becomes quite different in detail as it develops.

Old Honey lived with his wife in a little hut of two rooms and a talfat [a half-floor at one end of a cottage, on which a bed was placed] on the cliff side of Trereen in Zennor. The old couple had half a score of children, who were all raised in this place. They lived as they best could on the produce of a few acres of ground, which were too poor to keep even a goat in good heart. The heaps of crogans [limpet shells] about the hut led one to believe that their chief food was limpets and gweans [periwinkles]. They had, however, fish and potatoes most days, and pork and broth now and then of a Sunday. At Christmas and the Feast they had white bread. There was not a healthier nor a handsomer family in the parish than old Honey's. We are, however, only concerned with one of them, his daughter Cherry. Cherry could run as fast as a hare, and was ever full of frolic and mischief.

Whenever the miller's boy came into the town [farmyard], tied his horse to the furze-rick and called in to see if anyone desired to send corn to the mill, Cherry would jump onto its back and gallop off to the cliff. When the miller's boy gave chase, and she could ride no further over that rocky coast, she would take to the cairns, and the swiftest dog could not catch her, much less the miller's boy.

Soon after Cherry got into her teens she became very discontented, because year after year her mother had been promising her a new frock that she might go off smart as the rest, 'three on one horse to Morva fair' [local proverb]. As certain as the time came round the money was wanting, so Cherry had nothing decent. She could neither go to the fair, nor to church, nor to meeting.

Cherry was sixteen. One of her playmates had a new dress smartly trimmed with ribbons, and she told Cherry how she had been to Nancledry to the preaching, and how she had ever so many sweethearts who brought her home. This put the volatile Cherry in a fever of desire. She declared to her mother she would go off to the 'low countries' [the valley parishes] to seek for service, that she might get some clothes like other girls.

Her mother wished her to go to Towednack that she might have the chance of seeing her now and then of a Sunday.

'No, no!' said Cherry, I'll never go to live in the parish where the cow ate the bell-rope, and where they have fish and taties [potatoes] every day, and conger-pie of a Sunday for a change.'

One fine morning Cherry tied up a few things in a bundle and prepared to start. She promised her father that she would get service as near home as she could, and come home at the earliest opportunity.

The old man said she was bewitched, charged her to take care she wasn't carried away by either the sailors or pirates, and allowed her to depart. Cherry took the road leading to Ludgvan and Gulval. When she lost sight of the chimneys of Trereen, she got out of heart and had a great mind to go home again. But she went on.

At length she came to the four cross-roads on the Lady Downs, sat herself down on a stone by the roadside, and cried to think of her home, which she might never see again.

Her crying at last came to an end, and she resolved to go home and make the best of it. When she dried her eyes and held up her head she was surprised to see a gentleman coming towards her – for she couldn't think where he came from; no one was to be seen on the Downs a few minutes before.

The gentleman wished her good morning, inquired the road to Towednack, and asked Cherry where she was going.

Cherry told the gentleman that she had left home that morning to look for service, but that her heart had failed her, and that she was going back over the hills to Zennor again.

'I never expected to meet such luck as this,' said the gentleman. 'I left home this morning to seek a nice clean girl to keep house for me, and here you are.'

He then told Cherry that he had recently been left a widower, and that he had one dear little boy, of whom Cherry might have charge. Cherry was the very girl that would suit him. She was handsome and cleanly. He could see that her clothes were so mended that the first piece could not be discovered; yet she was as sweet as a rose and all the water in the sea could not make her cleaner. Poor Cherry said 'Yes, sir,' to everything yet she did not understand one quarter part of what the gentleman said. Her mother had instructed her to say 'Yes, sir,' to the parson, or any gentleman when, like herself, she did not understand them. The gentleman told her he lived but a short way off down in the low countries; that she would have very little to do but milk the cow and look after the baby; so Cherry consented to go with him.

Away they went, he talking so kindly that Cherry had no notion how time was moving, and she quite forgot the distance she had walked.

At length they were in lanes, so shaded with trees that a checker of sunshine scarcely gleamed on the road. As far as she could see, all was trees and flowers. Sweet briars and honeysuckles perfumed the air, and the reddest of ripe apples hung from the trees over the lane.

They then came to a stream of water as clear as crystal, which ran across the lane. It was, however, very dark, and Cherry paused to see how she should cross the river. The gentleman put his arm about her waist and carried her over, so that she did not wet her feet.

The lane was getting darker and darker, and narrower and narrower, and they seemed to be going rapidly downhill. Cherry took firm hold of the gentleman's arm and thought, as he had been so kind to her, she could go with him to the world's end.

After walking a little further, the gentleman opened a gate which led into a beautiful garden, and said, 'Cherry, my dear, this is the place we live in.'

Cherry could scarcely believe her eyes. She had never seen anything approaching this place for beauty. Flowers of every dye were around her; fruits of all kinds hung above her; and the birds, sweeter of song than any she had ever heard, burst out into a chorus of rejoicing. She had heard granny tell of enchanted places. Could this be one of them? No. The gentleman was as big as the parson, and now a little boy came running down the garden walk shouting 'Papa, papa!'

The child appeared, from his size, to be about two or three years of age; but there was a singular look of age about him. His eyes were brilliant and piercing, and he had a crafty expression. As Cherry said, 'He could look anybody down.'

Before Cherry could speak to the child, a very old dry-boned, ugly looking woman made her appearance, and seizing the child by the arm, dragged him into the house, mumbling and scolding. Before, however, she was lost sight of, the old hag cast one look at Cherry which 'shot through her heart like a gimblet'.

Seeing Cherry somewhat disconcerted, the master explained that the old woman was his late wife's grandmother; that she would remain with them until Cherry knew her work, and no longer, for she was old and ill-tempered, and must go. At length, having feasted her eyes upon the garden, Cherry was taken into the house, and this was yet more beautiful. Flowers of every kind grew everywhere, and the sun seemed to shine everywhere, and yet she did not see the sun.

Aunt Prudence – so was the old woman named – spread a table in a moment with a great variety of nice things, and Cherry made a hearty supper. She was now directed to go to bed, in a chamber at the top of the house, in which the child was to sleep also. Prudence directed Cherry to keep her eyes closed, whether she could sleep or not, as she might, perhaps, see things which she would not like. She was not to speak to the child at night. She was to rise at break of day; then take the boy to a spring in the garden, wash him, and anoint his eyes with an ointment, which she would find in a crystal box in a cleft in the rock, but she was not, on any account, to touch her own eyes with it. Then Cherry was to call the cow; and having taken a bucketful of milk, to draw a bowl of the last milk for the boy's breakfast.

Cherry was dying with curiosity. She several times tried to question the child, but he always stopped her with, 'I'll tell Aunt Prudence.' According to her orders, Cherry was up in the morning early. The little boy conducted the girl to the spring, which flowed in crystal purity from a granite rock, which was covered with ivy and beautiful mosses. The child was duly washed, and his eyes duly anointed. Cherry saw no cow, but her little charge said she must call the cow.

'Pruit! pruit! pruit!' called Cherry, just as she would call the cows at home; when lo! a beautiful great cow came from amongst the trees, and stood on the bank beside Cherry.

Cherry had no sooner placed her hands on the cow's teats than four streams of milk flowed down and soon filled the bucket. The boy's bowl was then filled, and he drank it. This being done, the cow quietly walked away, and Cherry returned to the house to be instructed in her daily work.

The old woman, Prudence, gave Cherry a capital breakfast, and then informed her that she must keep to the kitchen, and attend to her work there – to scald the milk, make the butter, and clean all the platters and bowls with water and gard [sandy gravel]. Cherry was charged to avoid curiosity. She was not to go into any other part of the house; she was not to try and open any locked doors.

After her ordinary work was done on the second day, Cherry's master required her to help him in the garden, to pick the apples and pears, and to weed the leeks and onions.

Glad was Cherry to get out of the old woman's sight. Aunt Prudence always sat with one eye on her knitting, and the other boring through poor Cherry. Now and then she'd grumble, 'I knew Robin would bring down some fool from Zennor – better for both that she had tarried away.'

Cherry and her master got on famously, and whenever Cherry had finished weeding a bed, her master would give her a kiss to show how pleased he was.

After a few days, Aunt Prudence took Cherry into those parts of the house which she had never seen. They passed through a long dark passage. Cherry was then made to take off her shoes; and they entered a room, the floor of which was like glass, and all around, perched on the shelves and on the floor, were people, big and small, turned to stone. Of some, there were only the head and shoulders, the arms being cut off; others were perfect. Cherry told the old woman she 'wouldn't cum any furder for the wurld.' She thought from the first she was got into a land of Small People underground, only master was like other men; but now she know'd she was with the conjurers, who had turned all these people to stone. She had heard talk of 'em, up in Zennor, and she knew they might at any moment wake up and eat her.

Old Prudence laughed at Cherry, and drove her on, insisted upon her rubbing up a box 'like a coffin on six legs' until she could see her face in it. Well, Cherry did not want for courage, so she began to rub with a will; the old woman standing by, knitting all the time, calling out every now and then, 'Rub, rub, rub! Harder and faster!' At length Cherry got desperate, and giving a violent rub at one of the corners, she nearly upset the box. When, oh Lor! it gave out such a doleful, unearthly sound, that Cherry thought all the stone people were coming to life, and with her fright she fell down in a fit.

The master heard all this noise, and came in to inquire into the cause of the hubbub. He was in great wrath, kicked old Prudence out of the house for taking Cherry into that shut up room, carried Cherry into the kitchen, and soon, with some cordial, recovered her senses. Cherry could not remember what had happened; but she knew there was something fearful in the other part of the house. But Cherry was mistress now – old Prudence was gone. Her master was so kind and loving that a year passed by like a summer day.

Occasionally her master left home for a season; then he would return and spend much time in the enchanted apartments, and Cherry was certain she heard him talking to the stone people. Cherry had everything the human heart could desire; but she was not happy; she wanted to know more of the place and the people. Cherry had discovered that the ointment made the little boy's eyes bright and strange, and she thought often that he saw more than she did; she would try, yes she would!

Well, next morning the child was washed, his eyes anointed, and the cow milked; she sent the boy to gather her some flowers in the garden, and taking a 'crum' of ointment, she put it in her eye. Oh, her eye would be burned out of her head! Cherry ran to the pool beneath the rock to wash her burning eye; when lo! she saw at the bottom of the water hundreds of little people, mostly ladies, playing – and there was her master, as small as the others, playing with them. Everything now looked different about the place. Small people were everywhere, hiding in the flowers sparkling with diamonds, swinging in the trees, and running and leaping under and over the blades of grass. The master never showed himself above the water all day; but at night he rode up to the house like the handsome gentleman she had seen before. He went to the enchanted chamber and Cherry soon heard the most beautiful music.

In the morning her master was off, dressed as if to follow the hounds. He returned at night, left Cherry to herself, and proceeded at once to his private apartments. Thus it was, day after day, until Cherry could stand it no longer. So she peeped through the key-hole, and saw her master with lots of ladies, singing; while one dressed like a queen was playing on the coffin. Oh how madly jealous Cherry became, when she saw her master kiss this lovely lady. However, the next day the master remained at home to gather fruit. Cherry was to help him, and when as usual he looked to kiss her, she slapped his face, and told him to kiss the Small People, like himself, with whom he played under the water.

So he found out that Cherry had used the ointment. With much sorrow, he told her she must go home – that he would have no spy on his actions, and that Aunt Prudence must come back. Long before day, Cherry was called by her master. He gave her lots of clothes and other things, took her bundle in one hand, and a lantern in the other, and bade her follow him. They went on for miles on miles, all the time going uphill, through lanes and narrow passages. When they came at last on level ground, it was near daybreak. He kissed Cherry, told her she was punished for her idle curiosity; but that he would, if she behaved well, come sometimes on Lady Downs to see her. Saying this, he disappeared. The sun rose, and there was Cherry seated on a granite stone – without a soul within miles of her – a desolate moor having taken the place of a smiling garden. Long, long, did Cherry sit in sorrow, but at last she thought she would go home.

Her parents had supposed her dead, and when they saw her, they believed her to be her own ghost. Cherry told her story, which every one doubted, but Cherry never varied her tale, and at last everyone believed it. They say Cherry was never afterwards right in her head, and on moonlit nights, until she died, she would wander on Lady Downs, looking for her master.

Ann Jefferies and the fairies

Ann Jefferies was the daughter of a poor labouring man, who lived in the parish of St Teath. She was born in 1626, and is supposed to have died in 1698.

When she was nineteen years old, Ann, who was a remarkably sharp and clever girl, went to live as a servant in the family of Mr Moses Pitt. Ann was an unusually bold girl, and would do things that even boys feared to attempt. Of course, in those days everyone believed in fairies, and everybody feared those little airy beings. They were constantly the talk of the people, and this set Ann longing anxiously to have an interview with some of them. So Ann was often abroad after sundown, turning up the fern-leaves and looking into the bells of the foxglove to find a fairy, singing all the time

Fairy fair and fairy bright,
Come and be my chosen sprite.

The fairies were a long time trying this poor girl; for as they told her afterwards, they never lost sight of her; but there they would be, looking on when she was seeking them, and they would run from frond to frond of the ferns, when she was turning them up in her anxious search.

One day Ann, having finished her morning's work, was sitting in the arbour in her master's garden, when she fancied she heard someone moving aside the branches, as though endeavouring to look in upon her; and she thought it must be her sweetheart, so she resolved to take no notice. Ann went on steadily with her work, no sound was heard but the regular beat of the knitting needles one upon the other. Presently she heard a suppressed laugh, and then again a rustle amidst the branches. The back of the arbour was towards the lane, and to enter the garden it was necessary to walk down the lane to the gate, which was, however, not many yards off.

Click, click, click, went the needles, click, click, click. At last Ann began to feel vexed that the intruder did not show himself, and she pettishly said, half aloud –

'You may stay there till the kueney [moss] grows on the gate,
    ere I'll come to 'ee.'

There was immediately a very peculiar ringing and very musical laugh. Ann knew this was not her lover's laugh, and she felt afraid. But it was bright day, and she assured herself that no one would do her any mischief, as she knew herself to be a general favourite in the parish. Presently she felt assured that the garden gate had been carefully opened and again closed, so she waited anxiously for the result. In a few moments she perceived at the entrance of the arbour, six little men, all clothed very handsomely in green. They were beautiful little figures and had very charming faces, and such bright eyes. The grandest of these little visitors, who wore a red feather in his cap, advanced in front of the others, and, making a most polite bow to Ann, addressed her familiarly in the kindest words.

This gentleman looked so sweetly on Ann that she was charmed beyond measure, and she put down her hands as if to shake hands with her little friend, when he jumped into her palm and she lifted him into her lap. He then, without any more ado, clambered upon her bosom and neck and began kissing her. Ann never felt so charmed in her life as when this one little gentleman was playing with her; but presently he called his companions, and they all clambered up by her dress as best they could, and kissed her neck, her lips and her eyes. One of them ran his fingers over her eyes and she felt as if they had been pricked with a pin. Suddenly Ann became blind, and she felt herself whirled through the air at a great rate.

By and by, one of her little companions said something which sounded like 'Tear away,' and lo! Ann had her sight at once restored. She was in one of the most beautiful places – temples and palaces of gold and silver. Trees laden with fruits and flowers. Lakes full of gold and silver fish, and the air full of birds of the sweetest song, and the most brilliant colours. Hundreds of ladies and gentlemen were walking about. Hundreds more were idling in the most luxurious bowers, the fragrance of the flowers oppressing them with a sense of the most delicious repose. Hundreds were also dancing, or engaged in sports of various kinds.

Ann was however surprised to find that these happy people were no longer the small people she had previously seen. There was now no more than the difference usually seen in a crowd, between their height and her own. Ann found herself arrayed in the most highly decorated clothes. So grand, indeed did she appear, that she doubted her own identity. Ann was constantly attended by her six friends; but the finest gentleman, who was the first to address her, continued her favourite, at which the others appeared to be very jealous. At length Ann and her favourite contrived to separate themselves, and they retired into some most lovely gardens, where they were hidden by the luxuriance of the flowers. Lovingly did they pass the time, and Ann desired that this should continue for ever. However, when they were at their happiest there was heard a great noise, and presently the five other fairies at the head of a great crowd came after them in a violent rage. Her lover drew his sword to defend her, but this was soon beaten down, and he lay wounded at her feet. Then the fairy who had blinded her again laid his hands upon her eyes, and all was dark. She heard strange noises, and felt herself whirled about and about; as if a thousand flies were buzzing around her.

At length her eyes were opened, and Ann found herself upon the ground in the arbour where she had been sitting in the morning, and many anxious faces were around her, all conceiving that she was recovering from a convulsion fit.

A fairy caught

I heard last week of three fairies having been seen in Zennor very recently. A man who lived at the foot of Trendreen Hill, in the valley of Treridge, I think, was cutting furze on the hill. Near the middle of the day he saw one of the small people, not more than a foot long, stretched at full length and fast asleep on a bank of griglans [heath], surrounded by high brakes of furze. The man took off his furze cuff, and slipped the little man into it, without his waking up; went down to the house; took the little fellow out of the cuff on the hearthstone, when he awakened, and seemed quite pleased and at home, beginning to play with the children, who were well pleased with the small body and called him 'Bobby Griglans'.

The old people were very careful not to let Bob out of the house, or be seen by the neighbours, as he promised to show the man where the crocks of gold were buried on the hill. A few days after he was brought from the hill, all the neighbours came with their horses (according to custom) to bring home the winter's reek of furze, which had to be brought down the hill in trusses on the backs of the horses. That Bob might be safe and out of sight, he and the children were shut up in the barn. whilst the furze-carriers were in to dinner, the prisoners contrived to get out, to have a 'courant' round the furze-reek, when they saw a little man and woman, not much larger than Bob, searching into every hole and corner among the trusses that were dropped around the unfinished reek. The little woman was wringing her hands and crying, 'O my dear and tender Skillywidden, where canst' a be gone to? Shall I ever cast eyes on thee again?' 'Go ee back,' says Bob to the children; 'my father and mother are come here too.' He then cried out, 'Here I am, mammy!'

By the time the words were out of his mouth, the little man and woman, with their precious Skillywidden, were nowhere to be seen, and there has been no sight nor sign of them since. The children got a sound thrashing for letting Skillywidden escape.

The piskie threshers

Many an industrious farmer can speak of the assistance which he has received from the piskies. Long ago, the farmer who resided at C---, in going to his barn one day, was surprised at the extraordinary quantity of corn that had been threshed the previous night, as well as to discover the mysterious agency by which it was effected. His curiosity led him to enquire into the matter; so at night, when the moon was up, he crept stealthily to the barn door, and looking through a chink, saw a little fellow, clad in a tattered suit of green, wielding the dreshel [flail] with astonishing vigour, and beating the floor with blows so rapid that the eyes could not follow the motion of the instrument.

The farmer slunk away unperceived and went to bed, where he lay a long while awake, thinking in what way he could best show his gratitude to the piskie for such an important service. He came to the conclusion at length, that as the little fellow's clothes were getting very old and ragged, the gift of a new suit would be the proper way to lessen the obligation; and accordingly, on the morrow he had a suit of green made, of what he supposed to be the proper size, which he carried early in the evening to the barn, and left for the piskie's acceptance. At night the farmer stole to the door again to see how his gift was taken. He was just in time to see the elf put on the suit, which was no sooner accomplished than, looking down on himself admiringly, he sung

Piskie fine, and piskie gay,
Piskie now will flyaway.

The Small People's gardens

If the adventurous traveller who visits the Land's End district will go down as far as he can on the south-west side of the Logan Rock Cairn, and look over, he will see, in little sheltered places between the cairns, close down the water's edge, beautifully green spots, with here and there some ferns and cliff-pinks. These are the gardens of the Small People, or, as they are called by the natives, Small Folk. They are beautiful little creatures, who appear to pass a life of constant enjoyment amongst their own favourite flowers. They are harmless; and if man does not meddle with them when they are holding their fairs – which are indeed high festivals – the Small Folk never interfere with man or anything belonging to him. They are known to do much good, especially when they discover a case of oppressed poverty; but they do it their own way. They love to do good for its own sake, and the publication of it in any way draws down their censure, and sometimes severe anger, on the object whom it was their purpose to serve. To prove that those lovely little creatures are no dream, I may quote the words of a native of St Levan: 'As I was saying, when I have been to sea close under the cliffs, of a fine summer's night, I have heard the sweetest of music, and seen hundreds of little lights moving about amongst what looked like flowers. Ay! and they are flowers too, for you may smell the sweet scent far out at sea. Indeed, I have heard many of the old men say, that they have smelt the sweet perfume, and heard the music from the fairy gardens of the castle, when more than a mile from the shore.' Strangely enough, you can find no flowers but the sea-pinks in these lovely green places by day, yet they have been described by those who have seen them in the midsummer moonlight as being covered with flowers of every colour, all of them far more brilliant than any blossoms seen in any mortal garden.

The fairy tools; or Barker's knee

The buccas or knockers are believed to inhabit the rocks, caves, adits, and wells of Cornwall. In the parish of Towednack there was a well where those industrious small people might every day be heard busy at their labours – digging with pickaxe and shovel. I said, every day. No; on Christmas-day, on the Jews' Sabbath, on Easter-day and on All-Saints' day no work was done. Why our little friends held those days in reverence has never been told me. Any one, by placing his ear on the ground at the mouth of this well, could distinctly hear the little people at work.

There lived in the neighbourhood a great, hulking fellow, who would rather do anything than work, and who refused to believe anything he heard. He had been told of the Fairy Well – he said it was 'all a dream'. But since the good people around him reiterated their belief in the fairies of the well, he said he'd find it all out. So day after day, Barker – that was this hulk's name – would lie down amidst the ferns growing around the mouth of the well, and, basking in the sunshine, listen and watch. He soon heard pick and shovel and chit-chat, and merry laughter. Well, 'he'd see the out of all this,' he told his neighbours.

Day after day, and week after week, this fellow was at his post. Nothing resulted from his watching. At last he learned to distinguish the words used by the busy workers. He discovered that each set of labourers worked eight hours, and that, on leaving, they hid their tools. They made no secret of this; and one evening he heard one say, he should place his tools in a cleft in the rock; another, that he should put his under the ferns; and another said, he should leave his tools on Barker's knee. He started on hearing his own name. At that moment a heavy weight fell on the man's knee; he felt excessive pain and roared to have the cursed things taken away. His cries were answered by laughter. To the day of his death Barker had a stiff knee; he was laughed at by all the parish; and 'Barker's knee' became a proverb.

The four-leaved clover

Not many years since, a farmer lived at Bosfrancan in St Burrien, who had a very fine red-and-white cow called Daisy. The cow was always fat, with her dewlaps and udder sweeping the grass. Daisy held her milk from calf to calf; had an udder like a bucket, yet she would never yield more than a gallon or so of milk, when one might plainly see that she had still at least two gallons more in her udder. All at once, when the milk was in full flow, she would give a gentle bleat, cock up her ears, and the milk would stop at once. If the milkmaid tried to get any more from her after that, she would up foot, kick the bucket, and spill all the milk, yet stand as still as a stock, and keep chewing her cud all the time. Everybody would have thought the cow bewitched, if she hadn't been always fat and held her milk all the year round; besides, everything prospered with the farmer, and all the other cows had more milk than any of the neighbours. No one could tell what the deuce could be the matter with Daisy; and they tried to drive her to Burrien Churchtown fair, that they might be rid of her, as she was always fit for the butchers. All the men and boys on the farm couldn't get her to Churchtown. As fast as they drove her up Alsie Lane, she would take down Cotneywilley, through by the Crean, down the Bottoms, and up the Gilley, and be in the field again before the men and boys would be half way home.

One midsummer's day in the evening, the maid was later than usual milking, as she had been down to Penberth to the games. The stars were beginning to blink when she finished her task. Daisy was the last cow milked, and the bucket was so full she could scarcely lift it to her head. Before rising from the milking stool, the maid plucked up a handful of grass and clover to put in the head of her hat, that she might carry the bucket the steadier. She had no sooner placed the hat on her head, than she saw hundreds and thousands of Small People swarming in all directions about the cow, and dipping their hands into the milk, taking it out on the clover blossoms and sucking them. The grass and clover, all in blossom, reached to the cow's belly. Hundreds of the little creatures ran up the long grass and clover stems, with buttercups, lady's smocks, convolvuluses, and foxglove flowers, to catch the milk that Daisy let flow from her four teats, like a shower, among them. Right under the cow's udder the maid saw one much larger than the others lying on his back, with his heels cocked up to the cow's belly. She knew he must be a Piskie, because he was laughing, with his mouth open from ear to ear.

The little ones were running up and down his legs, filling their cups, and emptying them into the Piskie's mouth. Hundreds of others were on Daisy's back, scratching her rump, and tickling her round the horns and behind the ears. Others were smoothing down every hair of her shining coat into place.

The cows were in the field called Park-an-Ventan, close under the house. Her mistress came out into the garden between the field and the house, and called to know what was keeping the maid so long. When the maid told what she had seen, her mistress said she couldn't believe her unless she had found a four-leaved grass. Then the maid thought of the handful of grass in the head of her hat. In looking it over by the candlelight, she found a bunch of three-leaved grass, and one stem with four leaves. They knew that it was nothing strange that she should see the Small People, but they didn't know what plan to take to get rid of them, so that they might have the whole of Daisy's milk, till the mistress told her mother about it. Her mother was a very notable old dame, who lived in Churchtown. The old woman knew all about witches, fairies, and such things; was noted for being a sharp, careful old body; for when she happened to break the eye of her stocking darning-needle she would take it to the blacksmith that he might put a new eye to it. The smith always charged her twopence. She would rather pay that than throw it away.

Our Betty told her daughter that everybody knowed that the Small People couldn't abide the smell of fish, nor the savour of salt or grease; and advised her to rub the cow's udder with fish brine to drive the Small People away. Well, she did what her mammy told her to do. Better she had let it alone. From that time Daisy would yield all her milk, but she hadn't the half, nor quarter, so much as before, but took up her udder, so that one could hardly see it below her flanks. Every evening, as soon as the stars began to twinkle the cow would go round the fields bleating and crying as if she had lost her calf; she became hair-pitched and pined away to skin and bone before the next Burrien fair, when she was driven to Churchtown and sold for next to nothing. I don't know what became of her afterwards; but nothing throve with the farmer, after his wife had driven the Small People away, as it did before.

The fairy funeral

The parish church of Lelant is curiously situated amidst hills of blown sand, near the entrance of the creek of Hayle. The sandy waste around the church is called the Towen; and this place was long the scene of the midnight gambols of the Small People. In the adjoining village – or, as it is called in Cornwall, the Church-town – lived an old woman who had been, according to her own statement, a frequent witness to the use made by the fairies of the Towen. Her husband, also, had seen some extraordinary scenes on the same spot. From her – to me, oft-repeated – description I get the following tale.

It was the fishing season; and Richard had been to St Ives for some fish.

He was returning, laden with pilchards, on a beautiful moonlight night; and, as he ascended the hill from St Ives, he thought he heard the bell of Lelant church tolling. Upon a nearer approach, he saw lights in the church; and most distinctly did the bell toll – not with its usual clear sound, but dull and heavy, as if it had been muffled, scarcely awakening any echo.

Richard walked towards the church, and cautiously, but not without fear, approaching one of the windows, looked in. At first he could not perceive anyone within, nor discover whence the light came by which everything was so distinctly illuminated. At length he saw, moving along the centre aisle, a funeral procession. The little people who crowded the aisle, although they all looked very sorrowful, were not dressed in any mourning garments – so far from it, they wore wreaths of little roses, and carried branches of the blossoming myrtle. Richard beheld the bier borne between six – whether men or women he could not tell – but he saw that the face of the corpse was that of a beautiful female, smaller than the smallest child's doll. It was, Richard said, 'as if it were a dead seraph', so very lovely did it appear to him. The body was covered with white flowers, and its hair, like gold threads, was tangled amongst the blossoms. The body was placed within the altar; and then a large party of men, with picks and spades, began to dig a little hole close by the sacramental table. Their task being completed, others, with great care, removed the body and placed it in the hole. The entire company crowded around, eager to catch a parting glimpse of that beautiful corpse, ere yet it was placed in the earth. As it was lowered into the ground, they began to tear off their flowers and break their branches of myrtle, crying, 'Our queen is dead! our queen is dead!' At length one of the men who had dug the grave threw a shovelful of earth upon the body; and the shriek of the fairy host so alarmed Richard, that he involuntarily joined in it.

In a moment, all the lights were extinguished, and the fairies were heard flying in great consternation in every direction. Many of them brushed past the terrified man, and, shrieking, pierced him with sharp instruments. He was compelled to save his life by the most rapid flight.